No Nonsense Number

Fractions

Years 2–3

$\frac{1}{2}$

Suzi de Gouveia,
Jackie Andrews
and Jude Callaghan

essential resources

Title:	No Nonsense Number Fractions Years 2–3
Authors:	Suzi de Gouveia, Jackie Andrews and Jude Callaghan
Editor:	Tanya Tremewan
Book Code:	291A
ISBN:	978-1-877498-53-4
Published	2008
Publisher:	Essential Resources Educational Publishers Limited

United Kingdom:
Unit 8–10 Parkside
Shortgate Lane
Laughton
BN8 6DG
ph: 0845 3636 147
fax: 0845 3636 148

Australia:
PO Box 90
Oak Flats
NSW 2529
ph: 1800 005 068
fax: 1800 981 213

New Zealand:
PO Box 5036
Invercargill 9810
ph: 0800 087 376
fax: 0800 937 825

Website: www.essentialresources.uk.com

About the authors: Suzi is the enthusiastic principal of St Teresa's Primary School in Christchurch, New Zealand. She has international teaching experience and has had the pleasure of teaching in a multi-cultural environment. Over 20 years of teaching have enabled Suzi to develop a wealth of ideas and resources to best help children.

Jackie is an experienced teacher who has taught middle primary children in both New Zealand and the United Kingdom. As a mother of three young children she is taking time out of the classroom and is enjoying having the time to diversify.

Jude is an experienced, enthusiastic teacher with a passion for teaching and learning. Her teaching programmes are innovative and exciting. Jude has embraced the Numeracy Development Programme wholeheartedly. She has joined the No Nonsense Number writing team to share her deep understanding and wealth of ideas.

Contents

Introduction

This book is targeted at pupils who are working in Years 2–3 and includes child-friendly learning activities to encourage the development of these concepts.

This book contains two sections. The first section comprises of activity sheets to support the learning and consolidation of the concept of fractions.

The second section is comprised of activity cards. These templates can be used in a variety of ways to develop fraction knowledge through independent, individual and group work.

Answers have been provided where appropriate. In some cases, model answers have been provided while recognising that many variations may also be correct.

Curriculum links (Years 2–3)

Core learning in mathematics: objectives

Most children learn to:

Year 2

Counting and understanding number: Find one half, one quarter and three quarters of shapes and sets of objects

Year 3

Counting and understanding number: Read and write proper fractions, interpreting the denominator as parts of a whole and the numerator as the number of parts; use diagrams to compare fractions and establish equivalents

Calculating: Find unit fractions of numbers and quantities

Source: Adapted from the Primary Framework for Literacy and Mathematics 2006

Finding half of an object

I am learning to find half of an object.

Colour the shapes at the bottom and cut them out. Then place each one on the right whole shape to show half of the shape.

1.

2.

3.

4.

5.

6.

a.

b.

c.

d.

e.

f.

Find half of each object. Colour one half of each object. The first one is started for you.

1.

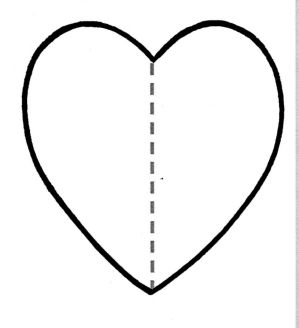

3.

2.

4.

Match the two halves of each insect to make a whole insect. You should get four whole insects.

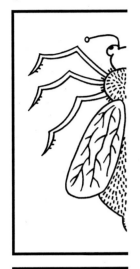
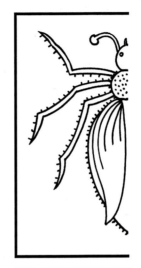

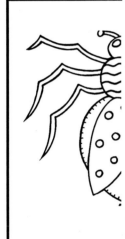
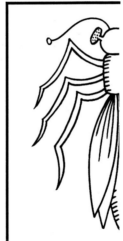

Cut out the boxes and match them to the correct half above.

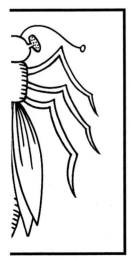
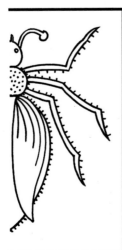

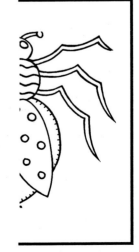

Nicholas has rubbed out half of each of these shapes. Make each one whole again by filling in the missing half.

1.
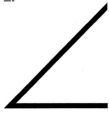

3.
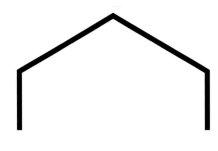

2.

4.
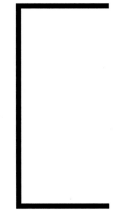

Now try these objects.

5.

6.

7.

Caitlin has rubbed out half of each of these shapes. Make each one whole again by filling in the missing half.

1.

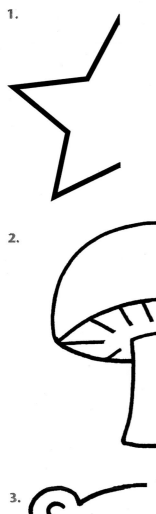

4.

2.

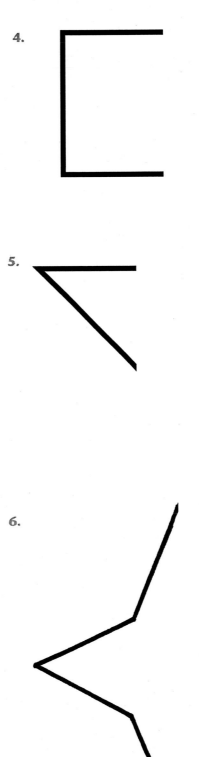

5.

3.

6.

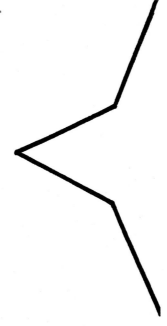

Recognising fraction symbols

Colour the shapes with $\frac{1}{2}$ yellow.

Colour the shapes with $\frac{1}{4}$ red.

Colour all the other shapes blue.

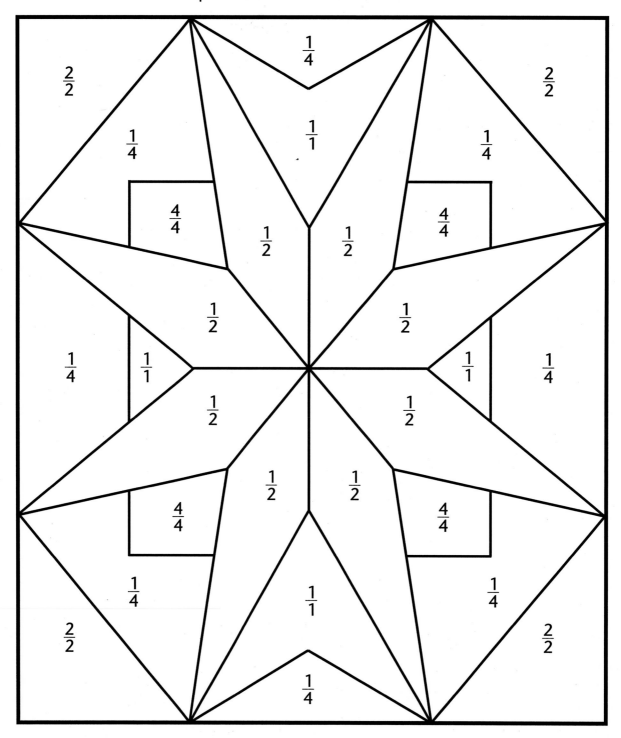

A. Colour the fraction symbol for: **one half** blue.
one quarter red.
one third yellow.
one fifth green.

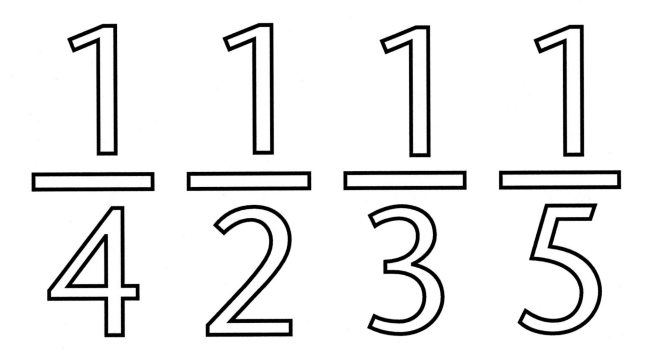

B. Colour the box to show the fraction.

1. $\frac{1}{2}$

2. $\frac{1}{3}$

3. $\frac{1}{4}$

4. $\frac{1}{5}$

C. What fraction am I?

1. Two of me make a whole. _____

2. I am the smallest fraction on this page. _____

3. Two of me make a half. _____

11

A. Colour the shapes with $\frac{1}{10}$ red.

Colour the shapes with $\frac{3}{10}$ green.

Colour the shapes with $\frac{5}{10}$ blue.

Colour the shapes with $\frac{7}{10}$ white.

Colour the shapes with $\frac{9}{10}$ orange.

Colour the shapes with $\frac{2}{10}$ yellow.

Colour the shapes with $\frac{4}{10}$ brown.

Colour the shapes with $\frac{6}{10}$ pink.

Colour the shapes with $\frac{8}{10}$ black.

Colour the shapes with $\frac{10}{10}$ purple.

B. Draw over the fractions in different colours. Cut them out and glue them in your book in order from **smallest** to **biggest**.

$\frac{6}{10}$	$\frac{9}{10}$	$\frac{8}{10}$	$\frac{5}{10}$	$\frac{3}{10}$
$\frac{10}{10}$	$\frac{7}{10}$	$\frac{1}{10}$	$\frac{2}{10}$	$\frac{4}{10}$

Colour the shapes with $\frac{1}{8}$ red.   Colour the shapes with $\frac{2}{8}$ yellow.

Colour the shapes with $\frac{3}{8}$ green.   Colour the shapes with $\frac{4}{8}$ brown.

Colour the shapes with $\frac{5}{8}$ blue.   Colour the shapes with $\frac{6}{8}$ pink.

Colour the shapes with $\frac{7}{8}$ white.   Colour the shapes with $\frac{8}{8}$ black.

Join the fractions in order from **smallest** to **biggest** to complete the picture.

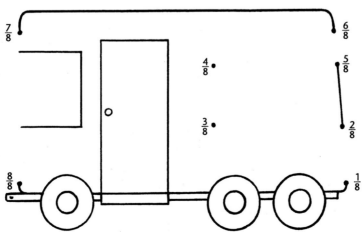

13

Finding half of a set of objects

1. Draw two fish in the goldfish bowl. Colour half of the total number of fish orange.

   Half of 2 is _____.

2. Draw six candles on the cake. Colour half of the candles purple. Colour the other half of the candles green.

   Half of 6 is _____.

Colour half of the objects in each set then complete the number sentence below.

1. $\frac{1}{2}$ of _____ is _____.

2. $\frac{1}{2}$ of _____ is _____.

3. $\frac{1}{2}$ of _____ is _____.

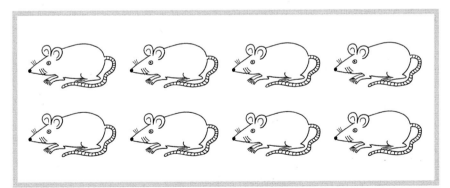

4. $\frac{1}{2}$ of _____ is _____.

5. $\frac{1}{2}$ of _____ is _____.

6. $\frac{1}{2}$ of _____ is _____.

Circle half of the objects in each set then complete the number sentence.

1. Half of ____ is ____.

2. Half of ____ is ____.

3. Half of ____ is ____.

4. Half of ____ is ____.

5. Half of ____ is ____.

Finding a quarter

I am learning to find a quarter of a shape.

A. Colour $\frac{1}{4}$ of each shape.

1.

2.

3.

4.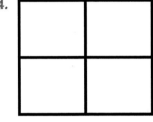

5.

6.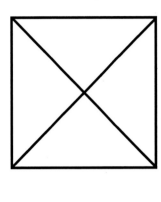

B. Find and colour $\frac{1}{4}$ of each shape.

1.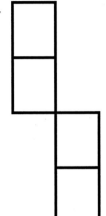

2.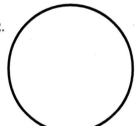

3.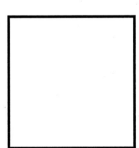

4.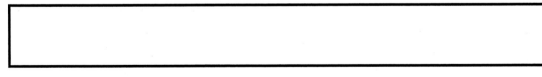

5.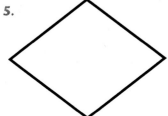

6.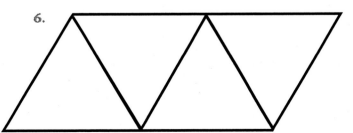

Cut the shapes out at the bottom of the page and stick each one on to a shape to finish it off. Colour a quarter of each completed shape.

1.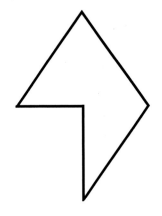

2.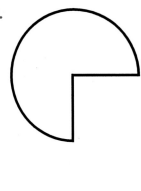

3.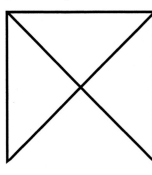

4.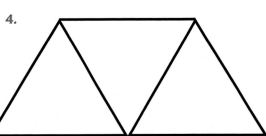

5.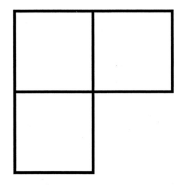

6.

---

a.

b.

c.

d.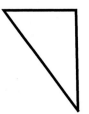

e.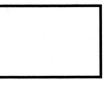

f.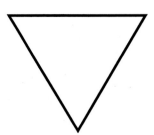

18

© Essential Resources Educational Publishers Ltd 2008

Colour a quarter of each set of objects and complete the number sentence.

1. $\frac{1}{4}$ of _____ is _____.

2. $\frac{1}{4}$ of _____ is _____.

3. $\frac{1}{4}$ of _____ is _____.

4. $\frac{1}{4}$ of _____ is _____.

5. $\frac{1}{4}$ of _____ is _____.

Equal sharing

I am learning to find a half of a set of objects by sharing equally.

Cut out the treats and share them equally between the boys.

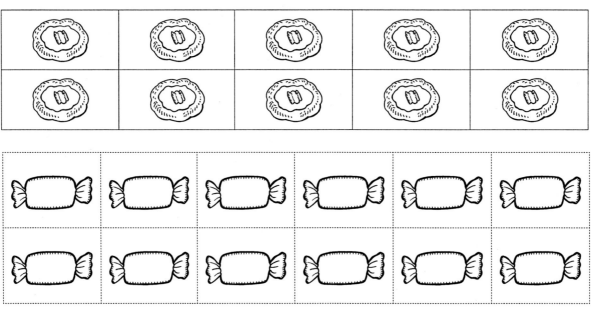

20

Help feed the rabbits. Cut out the rabbit food and share it equally between the two rabbits.

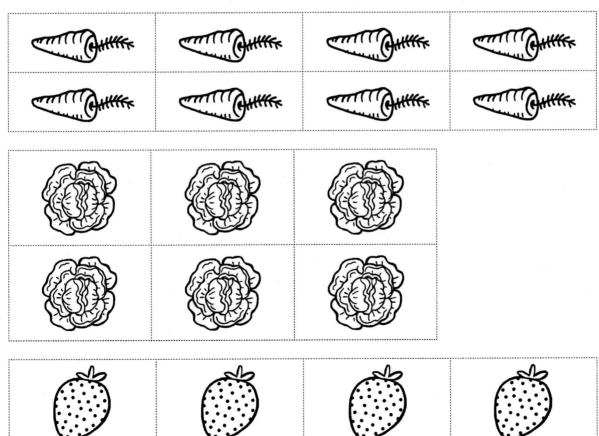

1. Count the eggs in this set. Colour half of the eggs. Fill in the missing numbers in the number sentence.

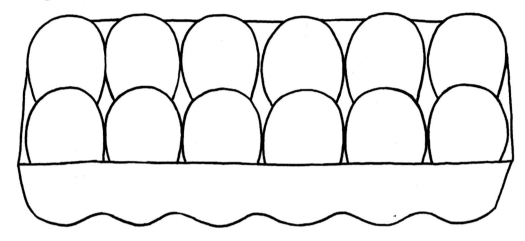

Half of _____ is _____.

2. Colour half of the dots on the clown's suit blue and the other half of the dots yellow. Fill in the missing numbers in the number sentence.

Half of _____ is _____.

Colour the rest of the clown in different colours.

Finding a quarter

I am learning to find quarter of an object.

Colour the shapes at the bottom of the page and cut them out. Then glue each one on the correct shape in the grey box to show a quarter of the shape.

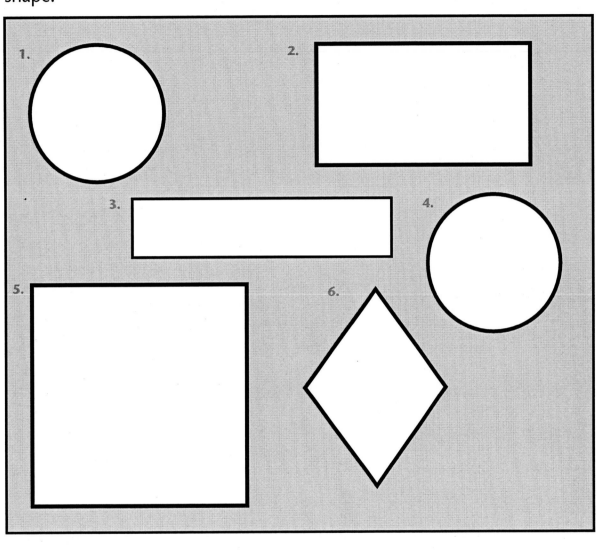

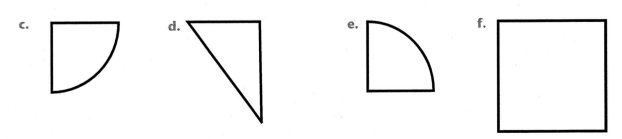

You have been given a quarter of a shape. Make the shape whole by filling in the three missing quarters. The first one is done for you.

1.

4.

2.

5.

3.

6.

Recognising fraction symbols

A. Match the fraction shown in the picture to its symbol.

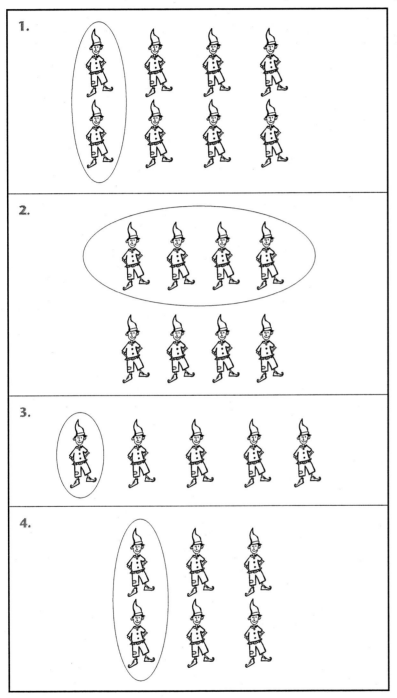

$$\frac{1}{2}$$

$$\frac{1}{5}$$

$$\frac{1}{4}$$

$$\frac{1}{3}$$

B. Draw your own pictures to show:

1. $\frac{1}{2}$ of a set

2. $\frac{1}{4}$ of a set

Cut out the basket and stick it below the correct hot air balloon.

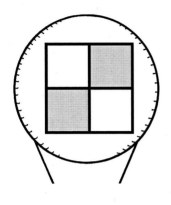
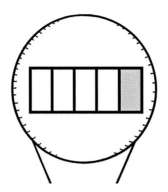
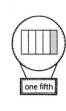

one fifth

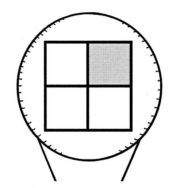

one fifth

one quarter

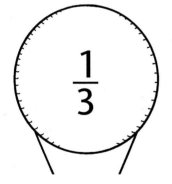

one quarter

one third

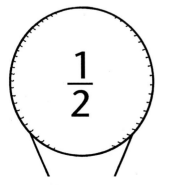
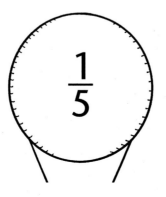

one third

one half

one half

© Essential Resources Educational Publishers Ltd 2008

Find the name, symbol and picture that show the same fraction. Colour them all a special colour for that fraction. There are four fractions so you should use four colours.

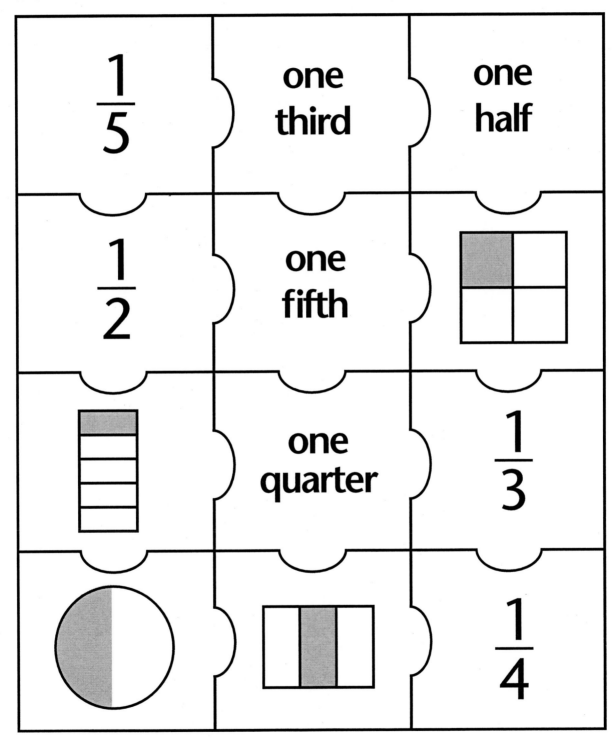

27

A. Match the fraction shown in each picture to its symbol.

1.

2.

3.

$$\frac{1}{2} \qquad \frac{1}{3} \qquad \frac{1}{4} \qquad \frac{1}{5} \qquad \frac{1}{4} \qquad \frac{1}{3}$$

4.

5.

6.

B. Draw your own pictures to show each of these fractions.

1. $\frac{1}{4}$ of a set

3. $\frac{1}{2}$ of a set

2. $\frac{1}{3}$ of a set

4. $\frac{1}{5}$ of a set

© Essential Resources Educational Publishers Ltd 2008

Writing fraction symbols

I am learning to write symbols for fractions.

Write the correct symbol for the fraction shown in each box. The first one is done for you.

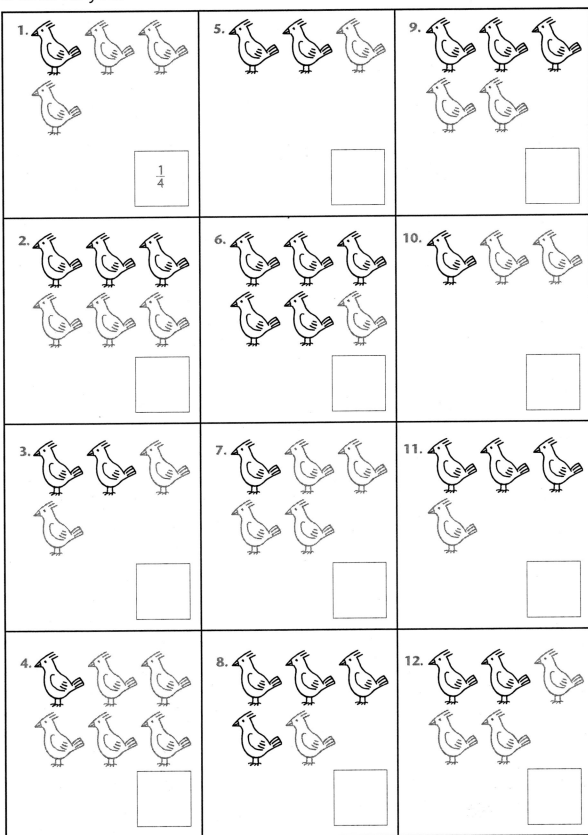

Finding a quarter

You have been given a quarter of a shape. Draw the missing three quarters to make the shape whole. Make each whole a different shape. They must fit in the space provided.

1.

4.

2.

5.

3.

6.

© Essential Resources Educational Publishers Ltd. 2008

Finding a fraction of a set of objects

I am learning recognise a fraction of a set of objects.

Complete the sentences. The first one is started for you.

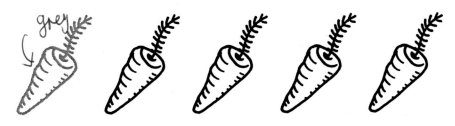

1. _____ out of 5 is grey. $\frac{1}{5}$ is grey.

2. _____ out of 3 is grey. _____ is grey.

3. _____ out of 4 is grey. _____ is grey.

4. _____ out of 2 is grey. _____ is grey.

Follow the colouring instructions then complete the number sentence. The first one is started for you.

1. Colour 3 carrots.

_____ out of _____ are coloured so _____ is coloured.

2. Colour 3 umbrellas.

_____ out of _____ are coloured so _____ is coloured.

3. Colour 2 honey pots.

_____ out of _____ are coloured so _____ is coloured.

4. Colour 4 bears.

_____ out of _____ are coloured so _____ is coloured.

5. Colour 2 caterpillars.

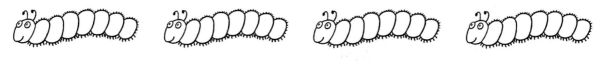

_____ out of _____ are coloured so _____ is coloured.

A. Show the fraction by putting a ring around the correct number of objects in the picture. Then write the symbol in the blank box.

1.	one quarter	🍎 🍎 🍎 🍎	
2.	one half	🐌 🐌	
3.	three quarters	🐁 🐁 🐁 🐁	
4.	one third	🧀 🧀 🧀	
5.	one fifth	✦ ✦ ✦ ✦ ✦	

B. Show the fraction by shading the correct number of objects in the picture. Then write the fraction name in the blank box.

1.	$\frac{1}{2}$ of these cars	🚗 🚗 🚗 🚗	
2.	$\frac{2}{5}$ of these hats	👒👒👒👒👒👒👒👒👒👒 👒👒👒👒👒👒👒👒👒👒	
3.	$\frac{3}{4}$ of these aliens	👽 👽 👽 👽 👽 👽 👽 👽	
4.	$\frac{2}{3}$ of these pencils	✏️ ✏️ ✏️ ✏️ ✏️ ✏️	
5.	$\frac{4}{5}$ of the tomatoes	🍅🍅🍅🍅🍅🍅🍅🍅🍅 🍅🍅🍅🍅🍅🍅🍅🍅🍅 🍅🍅🍅🍅🍅	

C. Shade $\frac{1}{3}$ of each of these shapes.

1.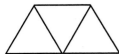

2.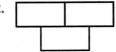

3.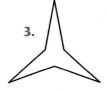

4.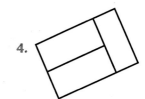

Equal sharing

I am learning to find a fraction of a set of objects by equal sharing.

A. Ben has three fish bowls and thirty three fish. He wants to put the same number of fish in each bowl.

1. What fraction will be in each bowl? _____

2. How many fish will be in each bowl? _____

He has 10 plants and wants to put two plants in one of the bowls.

3. What fraction will be in this bowl? _____

There are 24 white stones in his bucket. He wants to put three stones around the roots of each of the plants to hold them in place.

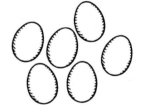

4. What fraction will be around each plant? _____

B. Complete these sentences.

1. $\frac{1}{3}$ of 9 is _____.

2. $\frac{1}{5}$ of 15 is _____.

3. $\frac{1}{8}$ of 32 is _____.

4. $\frac{1}{8}$ of 40 is _____.

5. $\frac{1}{3}$ of 30 is _____.

6. $\frac{1}{5}$ of 45 is _____.

7. $\frac{1}{5}$ of 30 is _____.

8. $\frac{1}{8}$ of 48 is _____.

9. $\frac{1}{3}$ of 21 is _____.

C. Now try these ones.

1. $\frac{1}{3}$ of _____ is 6.

2. $\frac{1}{5}$ of _____ is 7.

3. $\frac{1}{8}$ of _____ is 9.

4. $\frac{1}{8}$ of _____ is 4.

5. $\frac{1}{3}$ of _____ is 3.

6. $\frac{1}{5}$ of _____ is 4.

7. $\frac{1}{5}$ of _____ is 5.

8. $\frac{1}{8}$ of _____ is 7.

9. $\frac{1}{3}$ of _____ is 9.

A. Mum had four boxes of chocolates. There were 20 chocolates altogether and each box contained the same number of chocolates.

1. How many chocolates were in each box? ____

2. What fraction of chocolates was in each box? ____

Four chocolates were mint flavoured.

3. What fraction of the total number of chocolates were mint flavoured? ____

Ten chocolates were wrapped in gold foil.

4. What fraction of the total number of chocolates were wrapped? ____

Mum ate 4 chocolates. Dad ate 8 chocolates. Alice ate 2 and Bob ate 5. What fraction of the total number of chocolates did each person eat?

5. Mum ____   7. Dad ____

6. Alice ____   8. Bob ____

9. What fraction of the chocolates was left? ____

B. Complete these sentences.

1. $\frac{1}{3}$ of 12 is ____.

2. $\frac{2}{5}$ of 10 is ____.

3. $\frac{3}{8}$ of 24 is ____.

4. $\frac{2}{5}$ of 25 is ____.

5. $\frac{3}{8}$ of 32 is ____.

6. $\frac{2}{4}$ of 36 is ____.

7. $\frac{1}{8}$ of 56 is ____.

8. $\frac{1}{10}$ of 90 is ____.

9. $\frac{2}{4}$ of 18 is ____.

10. $\frac{1}{10}$ of 70 is ____.

11. $\frac{1}{2}$ of 82 is ____.

12. $\frac{2}{6}$ of 24 is ____.

13. $\frac{1}{4}$ of 36 is ____.

14. $\frac{1}{2}$ of 46 is ____.

15. $\frac{2}{6}$ of 18 is ____.

Finding simple fractions of shapes and lengths

A. Mum bought these jelly snakes. She shared each one equally among her five children. How many segments did each child get?

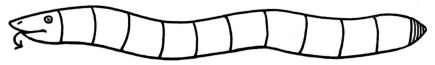

1. $\frac{1}{5}$ of 10 equals _____ segments.

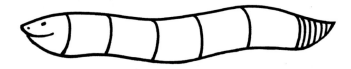

2. $\frac{1}{5}$ of 5 equals _____ segment.

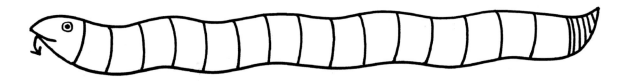

3. $\frac{1}{5}$ of 15 equals _____ segments.

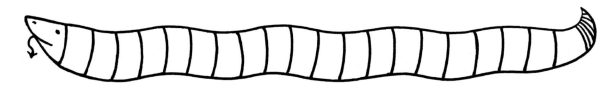

4. $\frac{1}{5}$ of 20 equals _____ segments.

B. Colour $\frac{1}{5}$ of each of these shapes.

1. 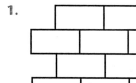   2. 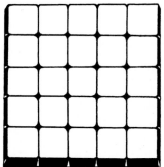   3.

© Essential Resources Educational Publishers Ltd 2008

Help the children share their liquorice with their friends by showing them where they would cut it.

1. I have two friends so I need to cut my liquorice into three pieces.

2. I have one friend so I need to cut my liquorice into two pieces.

3. I have four friends so I need to cut my liquorice into five pieces.

4. I have nine friends so I need to cut my liquorice into ten pieces.

Finding simple fractions of a continuous region

I am learning to find a fraction of a continuous region.

How many squares of chocolate did each child eat?

1.

I ate $\frac{1}{5}$ of a block of chocolate.

$\frac{1}{5}$ = _____ squares

2.

I ate $\frac{1}{4}$ of a block of chocolate.

$\frac{1}{4}$ = _____ squares

3.

I ate $\frac{1}{8}$ of a block of chocolate.

$\frac{1}{8}$ = _____ squares

4.

$\frac{1}{10}$

5.

I ate $\frac{1}{2}$ of a block of chocolate.

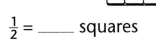

$\frac{1}{2}$ = _____ squares

6.

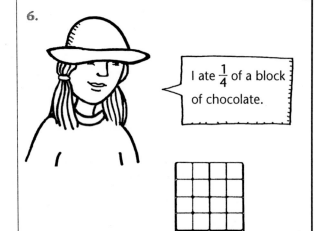

I ate $\frac{1}{4}$ of a block of chocolate.

$\frac{1}{4}$ = _____ squares

Activity cards

Sharing equally game (pages 40–41)

To **make:**

- copy the instruction cards (page 40) and children cards (page 41) onto coloured paper
- laminate and cut
- store in a ziplock bag along with 24 counters.

To **play** (in pairs), pupils:

- set out the children cards and follow the instructions on each card
- write number sentences on whiteboard or in an activity book.
- improve on their own score with each go.

Fraction bingo (pages 42–46)

To **make:**

- copy bingo cards (page 42–46) onto coloured card
- laminate and cut up
- store in a ziplock bag. The completed set consists of 60 fraction cards and 5 game cards.

To **play** with up to five players:

- each player has one game card
- fraction cards are shuffled and placed face down in pile
- players take turns to pick up the top card and match it to their game card or discard
- first player to fill in all blanks calls out "Bingo".

Fraction dominoes (pages 47)

To **make:**

- copy, laminate and cut dominoes (page 47)
- store in a ziplock bag.

To **play** (in pairs):

- one player shuffles and deals the dominoes
- the player with the shaded card begins
- players take turns to match the dominoes
- the first player to use all cards is the winner.

Pizza cards (pages 48–53)

The **aim** of this game is to develop the understanding that one tenth is smaller than one fifth etc.

To **make:**

- enlarge pizza cards (pages 48–53) onto A3 paper
- laminate and cut up
- store in a ziplock bag.

To **use**, two approaches are effective:

- Work with round pizza shapes **or** slab pizza shapes **or** garlic bread shapes. Hand out one of your chosen shapes to each child. Ask the children to order the sizes from smallest to biggest – or use vice versa – to determine the order of fraction pieces.
- **Alternatively** use the shapes to determine how many quarters in a half, tenths in two fifths etc.

Equal sharing

Take out 8 counters. Share them between the children. Write the number sentence in your books.

$\frac{1}{4}$ of 8 is _____.

Do the same with 16 counters
24 counters
12 counters

Use three of the children. Take out 6 counters. Share them between the children. Write the number sentence in your books.

$\frac{1}{3}$ of 6 is _____.

Do the same with 9 counters
12 counters
15 counters

Use two of the children. Take out 8 counters. Share them between the children. Write the number sentence in your books.

$\frac{1}{2}$ of 8 is _____.

Do the same with 8 counters   14 counters
12 counters   16 counters

Fraction bingo (fraction cards)

one quarter	one half	two thirds
three thirds	six eighths	three quarters
one quarter	four fifths	one third
three fifths	three quarters	four tenths
one half	one fifth	two quarters
two eighths	one third	two quarters
$\frac{1}{2}$	$\frac{1}{5}$	$\frac{1}{4}$
$\frac{6}{8}$	$\frac{1}{3}$	$\frac{2}{3}$

Fraction bingo (fraction cards)

$\frac{1}{3}$	$\frac{3}{3}$	$\frac{3}{4}$
$\frac{1}{4}$	$\frac{4}{5}$	$\frac{1}{3}$
$\frac{3}{5}$	$\frac{3}{4}$	$\frac{4}{10}$
$\frac{1}{2}$	$\frac{1}{5}$	$\frac{2}{4}$
$\frac{1}{2}$	$\frac{2}{5}$	$\frac{2}{4}$
$\frac{2}{8}$	$\frac{1}{3}$	

Fraction bingo (fraction cards and game cards)

	one quarter	one fifth

		$\dfrac{6}{8}$
	one fifth	
		$\dfrac{1}{4}$

Fraction bingo (game cards)

	one quarter	
		$\frac{1}{2}$
	one third	

		$\frac{1}{4}$
	four fifths	

Fraction bingo (game cards)

		$\frac{3}{5}$
	three quarters	
		$\frac{1}{2}$

		$\frac{1}{5}$
	two quarters	
		$\frac{2}{8}$

46

Fraction dominoes

$\frac{1}{2}$	$\frac{1}{2}$	three fifths	one fifth

two fifths	$\frac{1}{4}$	$\frac{1}{3}$	three quarters

$\frac{3}{5}$	$\frac{3}{4}$	one half	one quarter

$\frac{3}{4}$	one half	$\frac{1}{4}$	$\frac{2}{5}$

three quarters	$\frac{2}{3}$	one quarter	four fifths

two thirds	$\frac{1}{5}$	$\frac{4}{5}$	one third

Pizza cards

Pizza cards

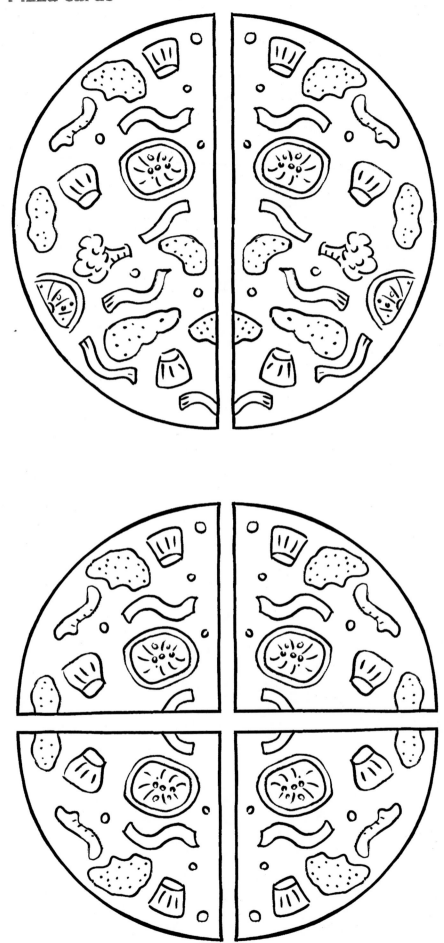

Pizza cards

Pizza cards

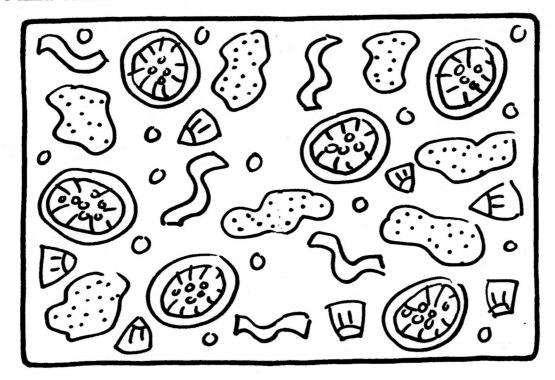

Pizza cards

Pizza cards

Answers to activity sheets

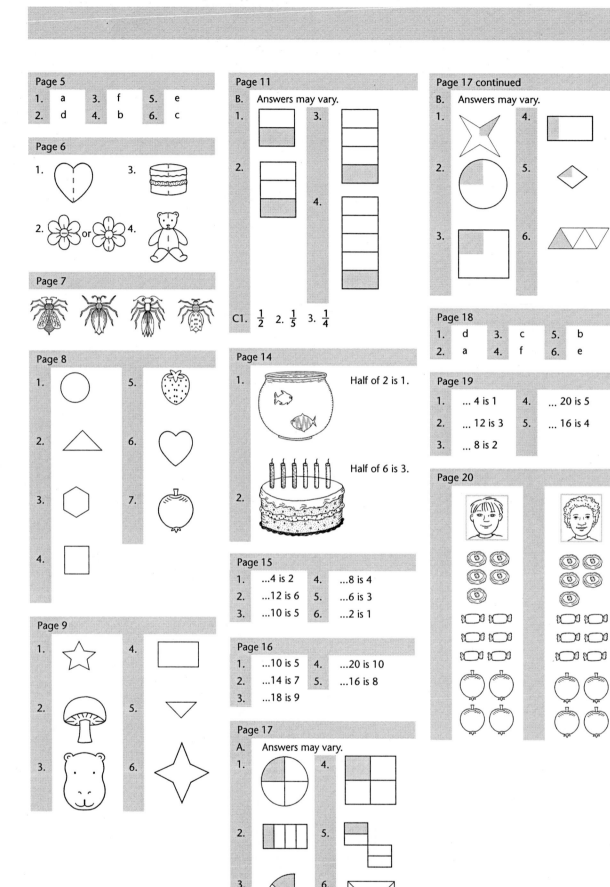

Page 5

1.	a	3.	f	5.	e
2.	d	4.	b	6.	c

Page 6

1.   3.

2. or 4.

Page 7

Page 8

1.   5.

2.   6.

3.   7.

4.

Page 9

1.   4.

2.   5.

3.   6.

Page 11

B.   Answers may vary.

1.   3.

2.   4.

C1. $\frac{1}{2}$ 2. $\frac{1}{5}$ 3. $\frac{1}{4}$

Page 14

1.   Half of 2 is 1.

2.   Half of 6 is 3.

Page 15

1.	...4 is 2	4.	...8 is 4
2.	...12 is 6	5.	...6 is 3
3.	...10 is 5	6.	...2 is 1

Page 16

1.	...10 is 5	4.	...20 is 10
2.	...14 is 7	5.	...16 is 8
3.	...18 is 9		

Page 17

A.   Answers may vary.

1.   4.

2.   5.

3.   6.

Page 17 continued

B.   Answers may vary.

1.   4.

2.   5.

3.   6.

Page 18

1.	d	3.	c	5.	b
2.	a	4.	f	6.	e

Page 19

1.	... 4 is 1	4.	... 20 is 5
2.	... 12 is 3	5.	... 16 is 4
3.	... 8 is 2		

Page 20

Page 21

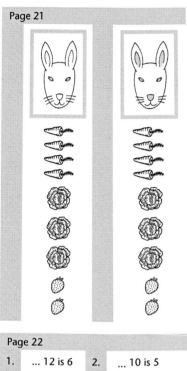

Page 22

1. ... 12 is 6
2. ... 10 is 5

Page 23

1. c or e
2. a
3. b
4. c or e
5. f
6. d

Page 24

2. 5.
3. 6.
4.

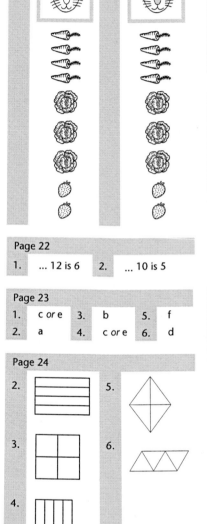

Page 25

A1. $\frac{1}{4}$ 2. $\frac{1}{2}$ 3. $\frac{1}{5}$ 4. $\frac{1}{3}$

Page 26

one fifth $\frac{1}{5}$

one quarter $\frac{1}{4}$

one third $\frac{1}{3}$

one half $\frac{1}{2}$

Page 27

one fifth $\frac{1}{5}$

one quarter $\frac{1}{4}$

one third $\frac{1}{3}$

one half $\frac{1}{2}$

Page 28

1. $\frac{1}{2}$ 3. $\frac{1}{4}$ 5. $\frac{1}{5}$
2. $\frac{1}{4}$ 4. $\frac{1}{3}$ 6. $\frac{1}{3}$

Page 29

A1. $\frac{1}{4}$ 5. $\frac{2}{3}$ 9. $\frac{3}{5}$
2. $\frac{3}{6}$ or $\frac{1}{2}$ 6. $\frac{5}{6}$ 10. $\frac{1}{3}$
3. $\frac{2}{4}$ or $\frac{1}{2}$ 7. $\frac{1}{5}$ 11. $\frac{3}{4}$
4. $\frac{1}{6}$ 8. $\frac{4}{5}$ 12. $\frac{2}{5}$

Page 31

1. 1 out of 5 ... $\frac{1}{5}$ is grey.
2. 1 out of 3 ... $\frac{1}{3}$ is grey.
3. 1 out of 4 ... $\frac{1}{4}$ is grey.
4. 1 out of 2 ... $\frac{1}{2}$ is grey.

Page 32

1. 3 out of 6 ... $\frac{1}{2}$ is coloured.
2. 3 out of 4 ... $\frac{3}{4}$ is coloured.
3. 2 out of 3 ... $\frac{2}{3}$ is coloured.
4. 4 out of 5 ... $\frac{4}{5}$ is coloured.
5. 2 out of 4 ... $\frac{1}{2}$ is coloured.

Page 33

A1. $\frac{1}{4}$
2. $\frac{1}{2}$
3. $\frac{3}{4}$
4. $\frac{1}{3}$
5. $\frac{1}{5}$

B1. one half
2. two fifths
3. three quarters
4. two thirds
5. four fifths

C. Answers may vary.

1.
2.
3.
4.

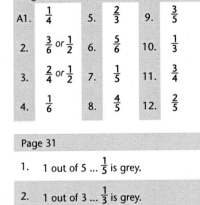
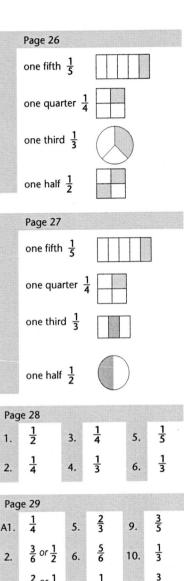
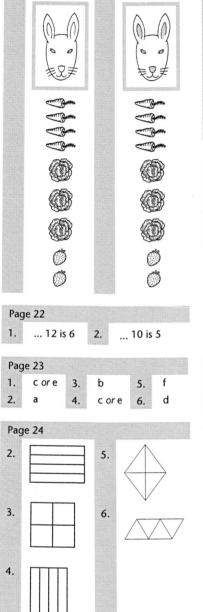

Page 34

A1.	$\frac{1}{3}$	B5.	10	C4.	32
2.	11	6.	9	5.	9
3.	$\frac{1}{5}$	7.	6	6.	20
4.	$\frac{1}{8}$	8.	6	7.	25
B1.	3	9.	7	8.	56
2.	3	C1.	18	9.	27
3.	4	2.	35		
4.	5	3.	72		

Page 37

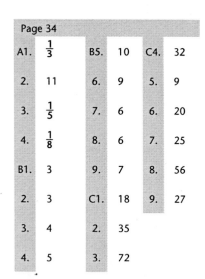

Page 38

1.	4	3.	2	5.	8
2.	5	4.	2	6.	4

Page 35

A1.	5	9.	$\frac{1}{20}$	8.	9
2.	$\frac{1}{4}$	B1.	4	9.	9
3.	$\frac{1}{5}$	2.	4	10.	7
4.	$\frac{1}{2}$	3.	9	11.	41
5.	$\frac{1}{5}$	4.	10	12.	8
6.	$\frac{1}{10}$	5.	12	13.	9
7.	$\frac{2}{5}$	6.	18	14.	23
8.	$\frac{1}{4}$	7.	7	15.	6

Page 36

A1.	2	3.	3	
2.	1	4.	4	

B. Answers may vary.

1.

2.

3.

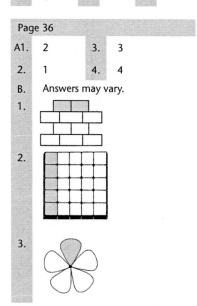